Xavier and his Magical Blueberry Muffins

By Anges de Sucre

Xavier liked to dream.
He loved to dream and bake.

Xavier liked nothing more than to
dream about cake.

Xavier's mummy however,
was partial to a blueberry or two.

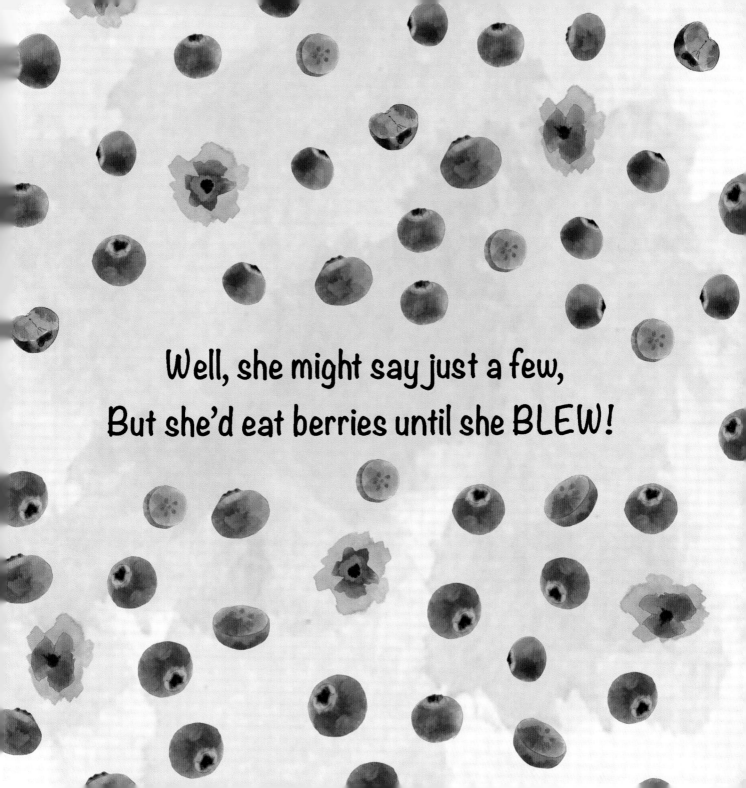

Well, she might say just a few,
But she'd eat berries until she BLEW!

Xavier thought his mummy would love
Nothing more than cake with a blueberry.

So he decided to bake a batch of magic muffins
With the help of his trusty teddy Terry.

Xavier grabbed a bowl to whisk up

One and a half cups of flour,
One and a half cups of sugar...

In goes a pinch of salt...

Oh! And of course, two teaspoons
of baking powder!

Terry cracked an egg into a jug

and mixed it with
five tablespoons of oil,

five tablespoons of milk

and a teaspoon of vanilla.

And whilst the oven was warming up
to a toasty 180 degrees,

Terry and Xavier mixed the wet and dry ingredients with a wooden spoon and squealed,

"This recipe is a BREEZE!"

But Xavier sensed that something was missing ?!

He looked in the cupboards,
and peeked in the sink...

He climbed on top of Terry's shoulders

And opened the
fridge,

starting to have some
niggling worries...

And there they were!

The punnet of plump and lovely blueberries!

A cup of blueberries
spooned into
the batter,

And a muffin tray
lined with 12 cases.

With the mix divided up equally,
now it was just the small matter,

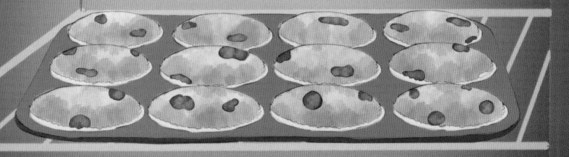

Of baking them for 20 minutes - whoa!
And the batter magically rises!

Yaaawwwnnn
That was a hard
day's work.

Off they went
for a nap,
Xavier with
Terry.

When we wake up and mummy smells the freshly baked blueberry muffins,

we'll be tucking into them, all soft and squishy, and be the most merry!

Recipe...